IN SEARCH OF SIMPLE

In Search of Simple

Field Notes from Near and Far on Slow Living
Edited by Heidi Barr & L.M. Browning

WAYFARER BOOKS
BERKSHIRE MOUNTAINS, MASSACHUSETTS

WAYFARER BOOKS
WWW.WAYFARERBOOKS.ORG

Published in 2023 by Wayfarer Books
Cover Design and Interior Design by Leslie M. Browning
Cover Image © John Forson
TRADE PAPERBACK 978-1-956368-27-7
HARDCOVER 978-1-956368-44-4

10 9 8 7 6 5 4 3 2 1

Look for our titles in paperback, ebook, and audiobook wherever books are sold.
Wholesale offerings for retailers available through Ingram.

Wayfarer Books is committed to ecological stewardship. We greatly value the
natural environment and invest in environmental conservation. For each book
purchased in our online store we plant one tree.

PO Box 1601, Northampton, MA 01060	
860.574.5847	info@homeboundpublications.com

HOMEBOUNDPUBLICATIONS.COM & WAYFARERBOOKS.ORG

Contents

In Loving Memory of David K. Leff

I t's about pulling back to a place where you can find the breathing space to be free and human again. From that, all else follows, if you can pay attention.

—PAUL KINGSNORTH

Introduction

What does it take to "live simply"? Sounds easy enough, but when we dig deeper into what drives the actions of human beings, it gets a little more complicated.

We're with Hank Lentfer when he says, "I want to grow carrots not because agribusiness is a filthy, greedy, heartless beast, but because rooting in the dirt is fun, worms are groovy creatures, and you can't buy the sweet satisfaction of a fresh carrot at any price. I want to live a simple, rooted life not because a place of privilege feeds on other people's poverty, but because meals of venison, potatoes, and berry pie fill our kitchen with gratitude-crazed grins. I want to leave the car in the driveway not because the carbon spilling from the exhaust will tip the planet into an inferno, but because a bike ride puts wind in your face and birdsong in your ears. It pumps blood through your veins and reminds us that life is a dizzyingly splendid idea."

Activist Jodie Evans once said, "Be in the conversation, not the fight," and those seven words have stuck with us as a mantra to live by (when feasible). The destruction left behind by big Ag and fossil fuel culture, as well as the premise of living simply so that others can simply live, are all great reasons to change our ways. But what about joy as a reason to change? Lentfer speaks of living true to his values because of the joy he feels because of his actions. He acts from beauty and a love of life, not from fear or anger or revenge. He is in the conversation, and that conversation leaves room for possibility. There are surely times to fight, of course, since a conversation takes at least two willing participants, and that doesn't always happen. But when there's a choice? The conversation opens more doors and illuminates more pathways than a fight ever could.

What if we discovered that changing our ways could lead to more beauty and more joy than we thought possible? What if living life (simply) really is a dizzyingly splendid idea? Just think of what would happen if more of us grew carrots and felt the wind on our faces and let birdsong be the soundtrack to life.

This anthology explores what it can look like to seek out slow living and embrace a life steeped in intentionality. Whether it's navigating grief to decluttering a home or habits to processing trauma, the writers in these pages have a wide variety of lived experiences and approach simple living differently–but they all end up in the same place: living the life they are made to live. You'll move from Romania to Colorado to New Zealand to Minnesota to New England to Canada with these writers, and by doing so, you'll see that there are folks in search of simple, scattered near and far. We hope this anthology inspires you to find the pace of life that sets you up to best contribute to the healing of the world.

Heidi Barr & L.M. Browning

A Case for Slow Living
Heidi Barr

Find solace in seasonal
rhythms of ritual, in ceremonies
of the ordinary.
Pull weeds, line-dry clothes, make jam,
walk to the mailbox.
There is much to savor
in slowness, when quality
of attention allows noticing
each detail–
intimacy with soil
soft flutters of well-worn shirts
hands and berries creating together
grass getting dewy in moonlight.
Celebrate this stroll
through the everyday,
this chance
to do it differently,
to revel in the slowness
that allows you
to pay attention
to the way the breeze
blows softly across your face
carries seeds to new homes

converses with branches
dances with tall grass,
reminding you Earth
is a living, vibrant
breathing thing
of which you
are a part.

October Exhale

Heidi Barr

October 6. I've just finished wiping off the jars of applesauce that I canned this morning. Late afternoon sunlight shines through the leaves, creating dancing shadows thanks to a brisk wind. It's not quite the peak of autumn color yet, but some trees are blazing red and orange. I like this time of year, despite feelings of busyness due to yard and garden work, the quest to acquire enough firewood, and winterizing things. Squashes are ripe, and there are still green vegetables to enjoy straight from the earth. It may freeze next week, so it's been a time of roasting, freezing, and baking to preserve the harvest. It's a time of abundance even though time can feel scarce. I inhale and keep working.

October 12. The first snow of autumn is here–just a dusting that's melting as the evening air grows just warm enough. Wind whips my hair around my face when I venture outside for a few minutes, and the fully yellowed maples are quickly losing leaves. Everything is damp and a little droopy, but the freeze hasn't yet come. Peppers and tomatoes are still fruiting, and some have new blossoms, even this late in the season. They're hanging on despite the fact they won't reach maturity. Back inside the internet is down. This is a welcome, if not wanted, respite from too much virtual connection. An empty muffin tin waits on the counter for batter. The sky is flat gray, but tiny water droplets dot fallen leaves on the grass, each one a world in itself, a world of cyclical light, a world of transition and turning.

October 14. Brilliant light bounces off of gold foliage, reminding me that autumnal evening paddling is nothing short of astonishing. I can see my breath as the air cools. The sun dips behind the trees as I paddle back toward the dock. In the shallows I see an enormous snapping turtle just under the surface of the water, near some decomposing lily pads. She swims right under the canoe. Her presence reminds me of all the life that exists outside my window, outside my screens, outside my human-focused agenda. She makes me want to be a better human, a better planetary neighbor, a better ancestor. She is a part of me, and she deserves a chance to thrive in clean waters, undisturbed. She makes me think about climate disruption and colonization and how badly humans still treat one another and the planet. What is my role in reparations toward the marginalized groups of people who are alive now? How do I best show up in daily life as an anti-racist, as a person who accepts where and when I entered the collective story? What does it mean to be a good ancestor? How do I move in wider circles? How do I live slower in a world that seems to speed up with every passing moment?

There are no clear, easy answers to these questions. Yet it remains important to ask them. And ask them again and again until a way forward is carved from the persistent effort to change the dominant cultural narrative for good. My ancestors came from a land across the sea, land I have never visited. But I live here, now, on land where primarily Dakota and Ojibwe people lived (and, of course, many of their descendants still do) until European settlers colonized it. It's land to which I feel connected, even with its complicated history. I must keep asking the questions and listening to the answers that may well be discerned from very different actions: Paying attention to the pause between gusts of autumn wind. Scouring the community for local stories that tell the true history of the land. Listening to the lived experiences of others, from humans to elderly snapping turtles, existing and persisting all these years as time churns on. Allowing slowness to be an acceptable speed at which to operate.

October 28. I am in the garden, hauling a bale of hay to mulch the garlic that was just planted. I look up at the sound of flapping to see eight sandhill cranes soar west to land in the field across the road. At 38 degrees, the air is cooler than it has been in months. Even though I'm not yet used to the cold temperatures, I'm glad for them. Planting the garlic always seems to signal a downshift from bustling autumn to early winter stillness. Most of the leaves have now fallen. Trees stand bare against a gray sky. Leaves that linger catch attention with flashes of burnt umber and gold in a long line of naked branches. Summer this year went by quickly, and it's hard to believe it's already time to change the routine from hoeing and harvesting to splitting wood and shoveling snow. But change comes, and we adapt.

October 30. The house is quiet, except for the crackle of fire and the soft sounds of a guitar. Flames reach toward the ceiling of the wood stove. Music expands into the empty spaces of the room. The house is cradled in darkness this late in the day. A car goes by outside, its dull hum barely discernible. What seems to matter is that in the foreground, that which is close at hand, within easy earshot or tangible distance. Things far away still matter, but in a different way (not more and not less) than what is happening right here, right now. I wonder if paying attention to what's right in front of me could be one way to cope with the uncertainty of the times, with the uncontrollable. I wonder if I can help make the circle wider by tending to my own roots, so I have the strength to extend my branches fully.

Flames continue to reach, and harmonies fill the empty spaces. The cats stretch out next to the hearth, content to sit still in the glowing warmth of the fire. Another log goes on. Flames lick higher and warmth reaches further. Days shorten. Nights lengthen. Time catches up to abundance, and I exhale into whatever's coming next. I hope I remember to move slow enough to inhale fully the goodness that awaits when I do.

Asking the Freeing Questions
Coming Down to Simplicity
GUNILLA NORRIS

"Tis a gift to be simple, tis a gift to be free, tis a gift to come down where we ought to be" . . . so the famous Shaker song goes. For me, coming down is the task of growing into more simplicity. It's not a matter of coming up with something wonderfully superfluous and new, but of centering down into a deeper sense of knowing what is essential and therefore to be truly chosen. To be simple of heart is to grow to know. It is not a knowing ahead of time. Therefore a good question can be a loyal friend. Like a slow snail it will carry its answer on its back, but it means dwelling with what scares us, what inspires us, what disgusts us and what forces us to make important choices for our lives.

I have had three ongoing questions that have helped me greatly. I consider them deep friends. I tuck one in my left pocket
and one in my right pocket. The third is in my heart pocket.
They are always there ready to help me out.

Whenever I am caught up in confusion, a disturbing reaction,
a need to make sense of things, or perhaps having to make an
important decision right away, I pause . . . . (those dots are a
symbol of making inner space). The habit of pausing and making space has taken a long time to establish. I believe it can't be
skipped if we truly want simplicity. Then, having given myself
space to feel and think, I take up the first question with more
willingness to listen and to learn. I ask, Is this mine? I am asking if whatever I am deciding about belongs in my life, if I feel
I have a responsibility for what is confronting me, and if I want
or need to engage? I am waiting for a gut response, which is
far different from a quick and perhaps thoughtless mental one.

The gut does not speak English, but it is wise beyond measure. It speaks in body talk. I have noticed that my lungs take
a deeper breath when the answer is yes. I breathe shallowly
when the answer is confusing and nebulous. I may even hold
my breath a moment when the answer is no. If I notice warmth
and excitement, I am inspired to say yes. If I feel a kind of
tummy dread, I know it's a signal that I don't want to be part of
what is being presented to me. My task here is actually obvious
and simple. If the answer is yes, I know to take up the task with
enthusiasm and willingness even if I sense things might get

difficult along the way. But if a tummy dread shows up, I know not to believe habitual thoughts like you ought to or you owe at least that. I need to say no, or at the very least give myself time by saying, I'll think about it. It has taken years to learn that my body never lies. It knows in a subconscious way and is very wise. That's true for everyone.

The second question that I like a lot follows. What is enough? I am always astounded by how accurately my inner self knows what really is enough. Like many, I may not always pay attention to that knowing, but it is there nevertheless. Asking what's enough can be applied to the amount of food I put on my plate, how much I spend in a store, how much time and attention I give to others, how much sleep I need, how I pile up chores on my to do list for the day, etc. That question always seems to apply and be useful.

I know most of us have seen babies push away food when they've had enough and don't want more. It's instinctual. Even though we cover it over much of the time, we haven't lost that instinct. We've lost coming down to it. That is really a time problem. We don't let ourselves have enough time to hear and feel the truth. The truth is already within us. We need time to sift down through layers of habit and reactive choices to the essence of what is enough for us. Mostly I think it's a few simple things. It is for me. Moving towards those simple things and living them fully will make us free.

The third question helps me with perspective. I need help to get out of too much me and into much more we. To work with this I ask, What would Love do? Asking helps me linger in unknowing and the realization that I am not Spirit's only resource. That lingering may not feel simple, but it is far simpler to let an answer slowly come with awareness of others and the issues at hand than to jump in, convinced that I know and by haste and lack of humility inadvertently do harm. I love how the Shaker song says to bow and to bend we won't be ashamed. There has to be a lot of mindfulness (bowing) and a lot of bending (cooperation) to get to simplicity and freedom.

Asking, What would Love do? is a courtesy question which encom-passes us as well others who are around us, and whatever is needed that can be done at the time.. Asking it, we are helped to come down to a larger and more inclusive answer. That answer will not be a black and white, either or one. But it will be inclusive and non-dualistic. The solutions will arise from within the situation. It's not easy to take the time to wait and slowly find what is right to do, but ultimately it will prove to bring about more simplicity and clarity.

Pausing in unknowing is tough on the ego. I know mine often sweats the process. The habit of pausing and asking is what has helped me the most. It has brought more simplicity into my life. Is it mine? answers whether I am to be engaged or not. What's enough? guides me in selecting how much to take in, how much effort and how much time to spend and still be in balance. Finally, What would Love do? suggest caring and mindful ways for me to go about whatever I choose to do.

Below are the words to the fine Shaker song that has been around a long time and is still completely relevant in our complex and troubled world.

Tis the gift to be simple

Tis the gift to be free,

Tis the gift to come down to

Where we ought to be.

And when we find ourselves

In the place just right,

'Twill be in the valley

Of love and delight.

When true simplicity is gained

To bow and to bend

We won't be ashamed.

To turn, to turn will be our delight

Till by turning, turning

We come around right.

Coming down is to be truly grounded in the here and now as well as grounded in body-wisdom-knowing, grounded in care for our selves, each other, and our badly aching planet home. Asking the questions that help us come down into more simplicity and freedom is more vital now than ever. That's what turning and turning is all about. Taking the time to savor the words to this old and relevant song you will notice the word gift. We can dispose ourselves toward more conscious simplicity, but when we have come down where we ought to be we will know we didn't do it so much as that we were led, that is, we were drawn deeper into wholeness. Our egos can't get us there, but the wisdom in our truthful interiority will nudge us along until we come around right. That is a big gift to celebrate.

Coming down to where we feel free and where we ought to be is filled with grace for then we will have been loyal not only to our bodies, but also to our souls. That turns out to be a bigger loyalty for it inevitably leads to being in some inherent ways loyal to others and to our shared world.

Summer of Mud
Gail Collins-Ranadive

The summer that the U.N.'s Intergovernmental Panel on Climate Change declared Code Red for Humanity was our Summer of Mud.

Mind you, my partner Milt had long intended to transition the yard into native grasses and plants: this third phase of intentionally moving away from fossil fuel dependency would actually sequester CO_2 emissions. Plus, landscapes with a diverse biomass also support native species, capture runoff, rebuild habitats, restore ecosystems, and save water.

But embarking on this mission had grown increasingly complicated... professional landscapers simply weren't interested in undertaking such an unconventional project. He'd finally found a young woman just starting her own landscape business in support of natural habitats; she would redesign his space and find workers to help implement the plan, though clearly Milt would be doing much of the work himself. Never mind that nearing 80 with underlying health issues make working outside in the high heat and smoke-polluted air a calculated risk. Yet we were now clearly in a global emergency!

And as elders who have been part of the problem, we feel called and compelled to be part of a solution. The climate has been steadily changing over our lifetime, and now scientists tell us there are less than six years left to cut global emissions enough to keep planetary warming within the goals set by the 2015 Paris Climate Accords. Yet feedback loops are already being activated ahead of schedule, with the current summer besieged by drought-exacerbated wildfires, flash floods, mudslides from burn scars, and unprecedented heat in unexpected locations. Code Red indeed!

Although I braced myself as best I could for what promised to be a summer of pure chaos as we implemented our personal response to the planetary crisis, I'd somehow spaced out about mud….

Not that I'd ever been fooled into thinking that transitioning into a more sustainable lifestyle would be as simple as flipping a switch: change is messy! And while installing rooftop solar on Milt's house was pretty uneventful, doing the same on my home back in Nevada ran into glitches and complications. But the hassles were worth it to be able to power our homes and run Milt's hybrid electric car without using oil or natural gas, a necessity for our species' survival.

In 2012, the crossover year when greenhouse gas emissions breached 400 PPM (350 PPM is the upper limit of maintaining life as we currently know it, our own included), Milt installed a geothermal heating and cooling system. Its construction process included drilling 300 feet into the ground and inserting pipes to exchange energy with the earth, where the temperature remains constantly between 50 and 60 degrees in the continental U.S. These pipes would become the house's organic 'roots'; in summer the excess heat in the house is transferred into the ground, in the winter the heat from the ground is pumped into the house.

Fascinated neighbors stopped by to gawk at the backhoe ripping up the front yard, often long enough for Milt to explain what we were doing, and why. (At least one neighbor put solar panels on his roof and bought an electric car.)

That project produced a leftover mound of dirt into which we put pollinating plants; it eventually spawned a maple and aspen grove in the middle of the front lawn. Now it was time to remove the rest of the lawn, as atmospheric greenhouse gas emissions surpass 418 PPM.

What's wrong with having a lawn? Everything, it turns out. Lawns cover over 40 million acres in the U.S., roughly the size of New England, and creates land that, for the sake of habitat conservation, might as well be pavement, according to Tyler Wells Lynch in the February, 2020 online issue of YES:

"Lawns, along with ornamental, non-native plants, provide very little viable habitat for native insects. This is because plant eating insects eat and reproduce only on certain native plant species, specifically those with whom they share an evolutionary history. And because bugs themselves are a key food source for birds, rodents, amphibians, and other critters, that dependence on natives-and the consequences of not having them-works its way up the food chain. Over time, landscapes that consist mainly of invasive and nonnative plants could become dead zones."

Increasingly unsteady on my feet, I was banned from the work site after a tumble that Olympic judges wouldn't have awarded more than a three. As my bruises healed, I appointed myself unofficial 'water girl,' and committed to keeping the (mostly female) crew hydrated. This simple task is complicated because we don't DO bottled water: the bottled water industry is relentlessly unscrupulous in how it tricks communities for access to their water, and the petrochemical industry that produces the plastic bottles irresponsibly creates toxic 'externalities' for employees and ecosystems to deal with, from cancers to polluted fishing areas even before discarded bottles end up choking the ocean.

My workaround? Glass mason jars with a different colored strip of duct tape for each worker held filtered tap water filled with ice that I kept replenishing as needed.

The 'as needed' continued through several mud episodes: dried mud, caked mud, wet mud, gooey mud, and stuck mud accompanied long hot mornings of trenching for the new irrigation system, sod cutting for the grow mounds, roto tilling of compost, topsoil, and squeegee, plugging the buffalo grass, placing of flagstone steps and walkways, then hosing everything down.

As each permutation tracked mud into the house, I swept it out again. It became a dance, an answer to despair.

"Why bother' and 'it's too late' haunted Milt's 'experiment,' and when, covered in mud, he'd come inside to rehydrate and regroup from hours, days, weeks of fetching materials from nearby hardware stores and hauling stone, breeze, and compost loaded into a homemade trailer behind his Volt, I'd taunt him with a threat to book us on a luxury cruise before he spent another cent on this folly. It's what seniors are supposed to be doing: we've been assured we deserve it. But we were peace activists when we met back in 1984, and have been climate activists since we became partners in 2010.

So this is the perfect metaphor for reinforcing our resolve and putting reality into perspective, what with a single cruise ship emitting more greenhouse gas pollution than one million cars, because it burns the dirtiest fossil fuel available to keep the engines running 24/7; it's not only a transport mode, it's a hotel facility, with the same energy needs as a small city, not to mention waste disposal demands. One trip could wipe out all our efforts to reduce our carbon footprint and make a mockery of our commitment to live as intentionally and responsibly as possible. As privileged seniors, we two choose not to use and abuse nature for our own pleasure just because our consumerist culture promotes it for capitalism's power and profit.

Despite being subjected to a lifetime of commercials relentlessly insisting that life on the planet is all and only about humans at the expense of other species and entire ecosystems, we do not regard the Earth as our personal cruise ship catering to our every whim and fulfilling our every wish!

A cruise is definitely NOT on our bucket list!

Rather, OUR bucket is one of those sold in home improvement stores. As I pour the left-over water from the mason jars into it, the yard dirt caked at the bottom becomes mud, evoking the primordial ooze it is said we all came from. It also reflects the muddle-headedness that precedes creativity, that impulse towards clarity that comes out of chaos. Within this impulse lies the human imagination that is needed at this critical moment in planetary history.

And I think I glimpse something dawning in the curious faces of neighbors and strangers who pause in front of the evolving mess that was once an ordinary lawn. Surely the species that developed the tools Milt is repurposing for his project is up to creatively dealing with the climate challenge of its own making!

Milt keeps working out in the summer-storm-muddied dirt, tweaking the irrigation system, putting in plants, and talking with passersby. A neighbor brings another neighbor who has already switched to native grass behind his house. Members from the church environmental group stop by on a break from gathering neighborhood apples for community use. When the little girl next door asks her perpetual question, "What are you doing," Milt invites her to help him hammer a nail into the wooden border he's constructing to go around the pollinating plant mounds.

As I deal with the latest mud invasion so the next owner won't have to, I imagine the children who will grow up here. Not only will they live on renewable energy instead of fossil fuels, they will be able to live simply, right-sized and in right-relationship with the earth, sharing this beautiful space with the whole life-sustaining ecosystem to which they belong.

Prayers and Whispers
Stephen Drew

There are seemingly random times while immersed in the ritual of deep-walking by the lake near my home, when I am given to remembering one such walk from long ago. I struck a deal then about the manner in which I might continue living. It was a deal made in desperation. I had no real leverage in the matter other than a willingness to try just about anything, because just about everything had been forever changed. There was not a single domain of the life I lived that had been left untouched; nothing had escaped the clutches of upheaval.

This great tearing-down, this disintegration of everything objective, was my most intense experience of grief ever, a tour de force of grief on an epic scale, a relentless cascade of loss bestowed in the period of a single year. And as I was left alone in the immediate aftermath, its first question to me, spoken in a surprisingly gentle and discreet voice, a whisper, was this: "Do you want to live?"

Despite all this, I recall having had a vague sense of being carried to this moment and that it was all somehow...perfect (if decidedly unpleasant). Even more strangely, it felt as if I was within view of an unfolding far horizon where something wonderful awaited. Yet between this moment and the promise of what was ahead, great attention would be required, a prayer of noticing, the practice of a new, solitary way of being in the world. Moving toward this, good quiet and a minimum of distraction would be essential. Discernment would require nothing less. Life itself was pointing toward a different paradigm, a setting aside of some things, a gathering of others.

Along the way of that long-ago walk, I came to an agreement with the fabric of all things dreamed and undreamed, known and wondered of, and wondered of again. It was signed in the innermost of places, in the midnight-cool quiet beyond everything sensed, in the place where trust lives and doubt goes to die, the place where true rest is all there is. Yet as pivotal and momentous as this agreement was, there was no fanfare of thought, no quickening pulse or pit-of-stomach surge. There were only the walk's following steps made with great assurance —hopeful as a first step, and certain as a last.

Left behind in the rubble were the objects of both mind and matter, things accumulated in attics and basements, things of distraction and false comfort, seen at last for what they were. Before me was a great revaluing, a new standard of what was necessary or desired, and no object was too large or small to escape the scrutiny of what truly belonged: Living space, furniture, clothing, work, relationships with self and others and the world, even thoughts, even memories...anything objective to the essential I (which meant everything), now held under new light and seen as never before.

The operating word then and now has been...simplicity. As electricity can only flow toward ground, I have sought the simple way in everything. Simple. Not to be confused with easy. Not to be confused with deprivation. And at the center of it all are some fundamental questions: Does this serve me, or does it not? If it does serve me, then how? What is its true cost beyond mere coin of the realm? Is this thing of the world being added to somehow augment what is already intrinsically perfect? Does the nature of this acquisition make it a thing of real and lasting value or of temporary soothing? Is something out there being brought in here to make the "in here" okay?

The primary clause in my new agreement concerned the placement of attention. And on that day, on that walk, I agreed to live a life determined less by what the senses and perception showed me, and more by the exceedingly subtle faculty of intuition, the deep knowing, the intrinsic divine, the still, small voice. I agreed that life would pray through me, that I would be its faithful dream, its obedient avatar, and thus would find all is well and I could rest.

As Thomas Merton wrote in Thoughts in Solitude, "Let me seek, then, (only) the gifts of silence, and poverty, and solitude, where everything I touch is turned into prayer: where the sky is my prayer, the birds are my prayer, the wind in the trees is my prayer, for God is all in all."

Having found myself abruptly released from responsibility to anyone, I was free to explore and express this new way of living without the burden of potential consequence to others. It felt right and authentic, and much of what has unfolded since has been miraculous.

These days, my walks are prayers—listening prayers of deliverance to what the high holy desires. They are prayers of good following, obedience, respect, and a generous measure of awe for what I've been shown is possible. They are prayers of surrender that do not ask why. They are prayers that fall easily through me because they make use of the best of me. Sometimes I'm shown to be mistaken, and then realize the voice of ego can be almost as soft as that of the prayer. Almost.

One good prayer called me to a far-away pilgrimage, a walk of 500 miles across ancient ground possessed of divine energy, wisdom, and transcendent grace—a much-needed walk, the epitome of simplicity itself. Upon returning home, another prayer called me to tell its story, a story to be shared through words put to a page. I believe such prayers can be heard only through devoted attention and minimal distraction because of their whisper, yet they are expressions of the great mystery.

And as I walked the prayer, I dreamed of the words that would arrive. I dreamed of how they may just fall into a book. I dreamed of all the eyes that would bring those words into mind and soul. And I dreamed of the words turned back to the world as pilgrimages of their own, prayers of their own. As

I walked, I noticed a steady, easy wind. It was then the words came and the book came and I was lifted to an answered prayer.

*   *   *   *

I suppose it could be said that had I not been living an austere, somewhat solitary life, those words may not have arrived, but I can never be sure. I do know distraction is the enemy of the muse (at least to me), and during that reflective time after the walking pilgrimage had ended, an old, nearly forgotten writing voice awoke. It had been so long, and I'd allowed myself to be led far astray. But a new section of the pilgrim's road opened before me in the form of the written word, and though my earliest steps on that road were tentative, certainty followed. As I wrote, it became clear that everything had been a gift—the life before, the life to which I'd been led, the words that came for others to read.

It's been quite a few years since that loaded time of grief when everything changed, when I was changed forever. But temporal life being what it is, things continue to evolve. If someone was to ask what I do with my days, I'd likely answer that I mostly wonder, and it's the wondering that makes way for words. The voice remains. The words continue. I've not yet said, "Amen."

Requiem for a Good Man
Joseph Little

You wouldn't know it to look at him, but Balrum had been sent home to die. A Nepali mustard farmer living atop Mount Sarangkot, he had left the mountains only twice in his life: once to participate in a census, the other to receive his diagnosis.

"It's his blood," his daughter told me, her eyes glazed by fear. "I tried to give him my blood, but they wouldn't take it. Said it would just run out of him on the inside."

There would come a day, the doctors told his wife, when Balrum would grow too tired to walk, too tired to stand, and on that day, she was to begin administering the morphine. Then he would sleep until he slept no more.

It was on this eve of dread that Balrum took me in, a wandering backpacker in need of a bed and a meal. He poured tea and invited me outside for a fire, arranging several chairs in a circle about a small patch of gravel. The white peaks of the Himalayas raged in the distance.

Before I knew his name or registered his physical appearance, I noticed the way he regarded the fire, with his full attention. He then directed that attention to me, warming me the way a father's approval might warm a son. And though others would soon join us and we would talk of many things, the whole evening took on a certain intimacy owing to his presence. Rarely have I felt such interconnectedness—not only with the people as you might imagine but also with the mountains, the moon, the sky unending. I felt the company of these inanimate objects as if they were beings.

It would take me years to understand my time with Balrum, and what I have come to is this: Well-being, at least for me, requires a sense of connection, connection requires presence, and presence requires that scarcest of resources among the moderns: prolonged attention. It is a tall order given that we live in a culture centered on the commodification and monetization of distraction, a culture that eschews intimacy especially among men, but I am making progress.

When I find myself hurrying through life, the mantra of our times—more, more, more—thrumming within, I often think of the way Balrum played solitaire with his daughter that afternoon, the way he regarded the fire and each of us that evening. Here was not a dying man distracted by a hail storm of thoughts but a deliberate man in whose sincere attention we all found time and space for the unfolding of deep relationship. Balrum was alight alright, but by the fire of his own contentment.

When I hatch a plan to eat lunch while scrolling through Twitter, the memory of Balrum occasionally intervenes and I stop to regard each bite, considering the cost to the earth of my consumption and the ways I will use the energy provided, a practice I have come to know as "noble silence." There are times when the moment expands before me, deep and rich, and I am sated by it because I am "there" for it. When I am present, I no longer have to check and recheck the front door because I was "there" when I locked it in the first place. The same goes for car doors and stoves. If I have FOMO for anything these days, it is the fear of missing out on the moment before me because I now see the connection between my absent-mindedness and my anxiety, not to mention the monkey mind that such absent-mindedness foments.

In short, when I am being picked apart by the birds of appetite, I remember the quiet man who in the season of his passing showed me a new way to love.

From a distance, the campfires on Mount Sarangkot look like constellations in the night sky. I imagine a young hawk soaring high above the earth, the patterns of Orion, the Pleiades, the Archer flickering overhead. Testing his abilities, the hawk dips a wing into a majestic half roll, then converts himself into a fearless inverted dive—only to find that what was once above is now below: another set of patterns, bright and shimmering. Vertigo arrests our young hawk, who finds himself disoriented, falling, tumbling through space and time until he rights himself by way of an innate fealty to the presence of gravity. May we all, individually and collectively, find our gravity.

Slow and Happy
Allison Sue Elliott

I was in my kitchen crying over a pot roast. Not because of the pot roast, as you might think. No, I was literally standing over it, attempting to check it while tears poured down my face.

My husband, Josh, had just gotten home from work. At the time, he was an officer in the Navy and often away for long hours–sometimes days. Having him there usually was a happy occasion, but on this day life felt overwhelming. Josh did his best to comfort me in the moment, but the more he inquired about what was wrong, the harder I cried… because truthfully, I didn't know. I didn't know what was wrong, why I was feeling overwhelmed, or how to put into words anything that was happening.

I only knew that this was not the life I was expecting. This was not the way things were supposed to be. Four years of careful planning, goal setting, and prep work had come to an end in one swift week.

The previous May was one I had spent years looking forward to experiencing. It contained graduation from my dream university, Josh's graduation from the US Naval Academy, his commissioning ceremony, our wedding, and the move to our first duty station. It was supposed to be the adventure of a lifetime. It was supposed to be the start of our American dream life.

It was all those things. It was none of those things. Everything my days had been consumed with in the last four years didn't exist in this new chapter. My time was no longer dictated by classes, my dreams had been fulfilled, and my goals were completed.

Navigating life began to feel difficult. It was difficult to adjust to married life. It was difficult to understand how I was supposed to show up as a Naval Officer's wife. It was difficult to be alone in an unfamiliar place. Worst of all, it was difficult to figure out my place in this new life of mine.

Looking back, I realize the tears I shed that night in the kitchen were the culmination of months of emotions I had not yet processed, could not explain, and did not understand.

I was 23 and this was my version of rock bottom–at least in comparison to anything else I had experienced up to that point. I felt guilty for feeling that way, because while a big part of me felt adrift, a bigger part of me felt I shouldn't have been.

My life was good, and I was grateful for it, but as my role in life shifted, my sense of self had become distorted. I felt alone, unsure of myself, and lost.

It was clear I needed to find myself again. I needed to forge a new identity and set new goals.

When that night ended, I knew a change needed to be made. At the time, the most logical solution seemed to be searching the internet for wisdom. While I admittedly did not find the answers to life I was looking for, my search did set me on a path to personal growth and self-discovery that forever changed the course of my life.

I discovered the idea of living intentionally rather than living for societal norms. For the first time ever, I paused to ask myself, "Who am I? Why do I do things the way I do? What do I truly and authentically want for my life?"

For a long time, I had thought the answer was to speed up so that I could get more done and build up my life. At some point, I realized it wasn't working the way I wanted it to. Years of "keeping up" taught me that when you rush, you miss things… the small things… usually the things that make life authentically happy.

I found that instead of speeding up to get more done, the answer to a better quality of life was to slow down. It meant establishing what being present, choosing happiness, and having grace for myself and others looked like. Authenticity became crucial in my life.

Figuring out what that looked like for me, finding myself, became my focus for a season. I read all the books, listened to podcasts, and attended conferences. As time went on, I made simple yet impactful shifts in our lives.

On our fifth anniversary, Josh and I sat down to reminisce over all we had experienced in the first years of our marriage and to dream about the future. We had lived in four states, moved seven times, and spent ten months living in hotels. We participated in a US Naval ship commissioning, welcomed a Chinese delegation, survived hurricanes, mission trips, deployments, and yet again, another move. We were grateful for it all, but we dreamed of simplicity, togetherness, and a place to call home. We had done chaos and were ready for a change. It seemed that life was better when life was simple because a simple life can be lived; a chaotic life is merely survived.

We talked of a life where we walked on our own land and felt the lush soft grass beneath our bare feet. A life where we felt good about the work we did and basked in the beauty of a quiet evening. Where long stretches of time were spent in breeze kissed hammocks and books were read by the fireplace.

We dreamed of slow and happy. A life where we were present, saw, and remembered the things worth remembering.

Then one day all our hopes and hard work collided when we accidentally stumbled across the most perfect little property. It was our dream – a little hobby farm. It was everything we wanted, and yet it was the scariest thing we had ever done. It's funny how when you finally arrive at the place you've dreamed of, hoped for, and planned out for so long, stepping into it feels hard. We had to choose to sit in the goodness and lean into the possibility. It was a new type of overwhelming. Overwhelming joy, gratitude, peace, and discomfort. As it turns out, peace and fear can exist simultaneously. You can have peace about your next step and fear of the unknown.

It made me wonder how many other times, before I had chosen an intentional life, had the thing I dreamed of been right in front of me, but fear kept me from it?

Perhaps, that's a benefit and the beauty of choosing intentional living – you slow down enough to follow your heart and soul to push past the way you have always done things – to do something different. For me, that is what intentional living is about at its core – stepping out of societal norms or habitual actions to be conscientious of the things around you and decisions you make that shape your future.

I won't say it was easy, as there were many bumps along the way and continue to be daily. Afterall, this is life we're talking about. What I learned is that intentional and simple living is not about never getting lost or being amidst chaos. It's just about knowing how to find your way back, so you don't stay lost forever.

My days are fuller than they've ever been. I work harder than ever before, but it's a simple kind of hard work. The kind that leaves you feeling good about your day and proud of yourself when you climb into bed at night.

At some point, I realized that an intentional and slow life is not about doing nothing every day, it is simply about giving space to what matters every day.

These days, intentional and slow looks like allowing the fresh morning air and sun to greet my upturned and accepting face. Saying "hello" to the animals and garden each morning and breathing in fresh dewy air that feels transformative.

An intentional and slow life is about stepping into whatever you choose for your life…whatever transforms you.

This is my version of intentional and slow. For me, living intentionally is about remembering to breathe because breathing is living.

Simple Living in Southern Colorado

Juliana Aragón Fatula

Today I woke to the sound of a crackling fire in the woodstove. My senses filled with the scent of sweetgrass and sage from my smudge bowl. I thought about my ancestors and how I came to this world. My ancestors lived in southern Colorado and northern New Mexico for thousands of years undisturbed by greed, corruption, and evil. They lived a simple life. So I have returned to the simple life to honor them and Mother Earth.

On my husband's sixtieth birthday, we drove to the high country to see the autumn Aspen and Cottonwood colors, and to reflect on how far we've come in our journey together. We met in Denver, on a blind date on his twenty-ninth birthday, thirty-one years ago. He is still my best friend of three decades, even though he's an outdoorsman and I'm an indoor woman.

We made it work. He worked as a high-rise window cleaner and drove a snowplow in the winter. I worked for the Colorado Department of Regulatory Agencies. We never imagined that someday we would become hunters, gatherers, farmers, recyclers, green energy consumers and live a simple lifestyle in southern Colorado. Yet here we are.

In Denver, we enjoyed the nightlife of metropolitan living, concerts, theater, museums, nightclubs, and weekend drives to the mountains. I volunteered and performed on stage at Su Teatro a Chicano Cultural Arts Center; my husband volunteered as a techie. The theater staff became our family. I toured for the Department of Defense in 1995 and performed on stages overseas every night for the sons and daughters in the military who serve and protect our country. That life was magical, yet it was the commuting to work on interstates and fighting rush hour traffic that led us to the decision to leave Denver. We traded a bustling, diverse community for my scenic, quiet hometown with one high school, one hospital, and one state highway running east to west, along with the chance to be near my mother after my father's death. Our backyard view encompasses the majesty of sunsets on the foothills that surround our canyon.

When we moved from Denver to Southern Colorado, my husband found work as a senior mechanical technician at the local hospital and today owns a business as a handyman. He provides us with a quality of life we never could have experienced in Denver, focusing on nature and sustainable living physically, emotionally, and environmentally. His work enables him to recover and recycle building materials, some of which he used to build our greenhouse, sunroom, and bookcases. His recycling has saved us thousands of dollars and kept glass, wood, and metal from landfills. Our friend who installs solar systems helped with our solar system and we received a rebate for the solar panels that feed the grid and sell electricity back to the power company.

The irrigation system my husband built pumps water from the DeWeese ditch from the Sangre de Cristo mountains. With the flip of a switch, our sprinklers come to life. We pump the ditchwater into rain barrels for use between watering days. We grow strawberries, raspberries, tomatoes, zucchini, green beans, peppers, and herbs. The native plants and flowers we've cultivated attract birds and bees. We feed the birds to encourage them to build their nests in our garden and the birds eat the bad bugs. The sounds of the water fountains and birdsong creates a magical world. We're careful not to get in the path of our winged neighbors as they soar through the garden building their nests and feeding their babies.

Come August, we collect wild mushrooms and dehydrate them along with apples, peaches, and tomatoes. The rest of our garden harvest goes in the freezer. My husband creates delicious teriyaki jerky from elk, deer, and moose–his hunting skills have supplied our meat for over thirty years. We camp in the mountains and enjoy the tranquility of our home on wheels we refer to as our love shack. We read, write, relax, and hike with our Border Collie and mini-Aussie. The portable solar panel and generator keeps the camper charged and supplies energy for cooking, heating, cooling, and showers.

My gardening, cooking, and baking have enabled us to enjoy the fruits and vegetables in our garden. I grow lavender for essential oils and yarrow for my homemade shampoo. I use cannabis for cooking and for medicinal salves for arthritis, depression, and creative energy. We compost the organic waste for next year's garden.

Our woodstove stays lit when the temperatures in Southern Colorado dip below freezing and keeps us toasty in winter fueled by the wood my husband enjoys collecting from the woods. We have deer that graze in our yard–one day a doe gave birth in our front yard! The fawns follow their mothers closely and I love to see them nursing and growing fat. The view from my window allows companionship with the resident wild things.

I'm able to write from the comfort of my home, and during this Covid pandemic I was thankful to be able to communicate via social media with other writers and workshop writing on Zoom. As I was working on finishing several writing projects, including digging into some personal history, my ancestors spoke to me. Through this research, I connected to the Ute, Navajo, and Pueblo people. How did they live, survive, and flourish in this part of the country? They nurtured the land, thanked the animals who supplied food for their families. They honored the great spirit and survived off the land. I am honoring their legacy by trying to do the same.

My great-great grandmother, Abrana Quintana, was Ute, and she married a white man from Massachusetts, the Reverend Albert Jacobs at Fort Union, New Mexico. The Indian Agent Lafayette Head traded Indigenous orphans to landowners for ranch hands, herders, farmers. He sold my great-grandfather, a four-year-old, to a family in Alamosa, Colorado. These Indigenous slaves called genízaros took their owner's surname. My great-grandmother married a full-blooded Navajo man, Jose Gomez, in Alamosa, Colorado.

A gambler murdered my mother's father, Miramón Mondragón, an Indigenous man born in the territory of New Mexico; my grandfather died over a card game and money. In the 1950's my paternal grandfather, Juan Aragon's, neighbors poisoned him because of jealousy and soon after my grandmother died young of cancer. My father, Julian Aragon, became the guardian to his nine younger siblings.

In the 1930's my mom's brother accidently shot her when she was a child while he was cleaning his rifle in the kitchen. The bullet went through her left and right calves clean as a whistle. Before I was born, my father's oldest daughter and ex-wife stabbed my mother, Eloisa Mondragon Aragon, and left her for dead behind the bar where she worked. She survived or I would not exist.

Then in 1978, my ex-husband held his pistol to my head in a failed murder/suicide because of a prayer and a song, *Jesus Loves Me*. I endured a recurring nightmare for years and sometimes if I say his name, I still have the deadly dream. In 1982, I asked for a divorce and my ex-husband kidnapped my son and hid him until I agreed to return. Generational trauma runs deep and is persistent. But my ancestors survived, and I'm still here.

And I'm strong because my ancestors gave me courage, wisdom, honesty, morals, traditions, spirituality, and love. I am the combination of all the years of suffering, fighting, praying, and sacrificing that made me able to empathize, sympathize, and learn from mistakes and create a new story. A survivor who never gave up, got up when knocked down, set goals to graduate first in my family from college, travel the world, to be a lifelong-learner and to heal the people with my stories.

We live in Southern Colorado and enjoy simple living. We carry the scars of our past, but those scars don't define who we are. Our actions define who we are. We heat our home with firewood we gather from the forest. We collect rainwater in barrels. We hunt, fish, and eat meat without preservatives, and we bake bread, tortillas, and eat frybread tacos. We enjoy our simple life and hardly ever miss the traffic and noise of Denver. We have created our own Garden of Eden and dream of the retirement years filled with abundance. We honor the past and teach the next generation to live simply. We continue to grow with purpose and intent to a lifestyle that does not deplete or poison the soil but nurtures and heals the planet.

It All Started At Home

Angie Kikstra

The memory is so vivid: We took a last minute Valentine's Day trip to the city for a hockey game and a stay in a beautiful hotel room in downtown Calgary. The spur of the moment trip was something Mr. Cozy (my husband) had planned. He knew how frazzled I was feeling at home and wanted to give me a break.

A calm washed over me as soon as I stepped into the suite. I walked around the kitchenette after dropping my bag at the door, I ran my hand over the countertop and on the backs of the chairs. I was drawn to the living room window that over-looked the city below. I stood at the window and looked over the downtown core and took the moment in... fully. I let out a sigh of relief. I remember a tear rolling down my cheek. This was the first time I felt like I could breathe in a very long time

At that point in my life I was exhausted.

The type of "exhausted" you get when day to day life feels like you are treading water. You can barely keep your head above water, but you have no choice. You just keep going. You keep going but everything is draining. You have a hard time waking up because your sleep isn't productive. You have a hard time falling asleep because your mind is thinking of all the things that you need to do. You need to keep going, treading that water, even though you're exhausted.

Even with all of this heaviness, I continued to add.

A new activity for my daughter so that she had a fulfilling and happy childhood.

That cute new trendy decor piece to try to make home feel like home (or at least look like those places online).

I bought more clothes because I thought they would magically make me feel better about myself.

An event committee for the town we lived in to help me feel like I had a purpose outside of our home.

A parent role at school because I couldn't say "no" or they might end up disliking me for not helping.

The weight of these responsibilities and things on my back made treading water even more difficult.

The odd thing is that I felt peaceful overlooking the hurried activity of the metropolitan core below me. I could hear the sounds of the street and yet, it felt calming.

My usual recharge spaces are quiet and slow, with few to no people. Usually a place in nature or in the country. So it was odd that this place filled me up.

I pulled back away from the window and realized the surroundings making the impact on my state of well being wasn't the city, it was the room I was in. It was the environment of the clutter free and calming hotel room.

That was when a lightbulb went off in my head.

That this could be recreated at home. Whatever was going on in the "world out there" wouldn't impact me in a calming and soothing space.

I didn't know how I would do it, but I knew I needed to get that same feeling at home.

From that point on my mission was to uncover a home that I could relax and unwind in, the way I did when I was on vacation.

I didn't just "want" that feeling at home.

I knew that on a deeper level, I needed it.

The journey did not come easy, I didn't just dump out everything in the trash and start fresh. Over the course of two years I removed clutter in layers and slowly but surely I uncovered a home that supported me and the life I lived.

I learned to say no quickly and yes slowly.

I removed more than I brought into our home.

I found that I learned so much from the journey that I was very careful about what occupied my time and space.

When my house was full, if I sat down I would fall into a cycle of feeling like I needed to declutter, tidy and clean, but being paralyzed by overwhelm. I'd feel shame for the way it was and guilt for not doing anything about it. This was a shame/guilt cycle that I played over and over in my head.

It meant that I would end up getting nothing done because I had no energy after mentally beating myself up for not doing what I needed to do around the house. Things like the dishes overflowing in the sink. The pile of laundry needing to be done, the pile of laundry needing to be folded and the pile of laundry needing to be put away. Not to mention the overflowing cupboards and stuffed surfaces.

Whereas now, I find myself sitting on the sofa with my morning coffee and just experiencing the moment. Listening to the birds through the open windows. Dogs beside me and at my feet, snoring gently. My mind is quiet and not consumed and distracted by a growing mental to-do list. I don't feel guilty about taking the time to recenter and energize myself each morning.

If I'm being completely honest, I probably sit and rest more often now throughout the day than I did before. My rest is more productive now. I don't feel burdened with house cleaning. The laundry is done once a week in one or two loads. The countertops are clear and dishes are done every night and put away every morning. The guilt and shame of a messy and untidy house is gone. My environment is more like that hotel room and feels calming and supportive with little effort on my part. Getting rid of the excess made daily upkeep easier.

Before I simplified, the mess at home affected time spent away from home too. I hardly left home because I was exhausted. If I managed to muster up the energy to go somewhere, my mind was always filled with the growing to-do list in my head. Even if I went out to spend time with family and friends… I would end up thinking about everything that I needed to do back home. The growing to-do list of responsibilities didn't end when I walked out the door. They were just as heavy as when I was at home, perhaps even more. I found no joy in the time away. Home wasn't a place of comfort. It was a piece of the stress pie.

Time feels like it's slowed down to a pace that I can fully take in moments. Our family enjoys camping, we often load up our holiday trailer and head to the mountains just west of us. Going for hikes, fishing along the creek or even just relaxing in front of the fire are all activities I can fully experience now. These trips are restful and regenerative for my soul. I find my-self in moments soaking in all of my senses. This is pure joy to me. This is just one of the many activities that simplifying my life has made room for.

When most people think of minimalism, they think of less. I like to think about minimalism as less of what doesn't matter, and the right amount of what does. It's a beautiful balance, be-cause either extreme doesn't work for me. Our home is a cozy and calming home that we can relax, unwind and recharge in. I had a friend describe it as a big hug.

Here's the beauty of simplifying your home and life. You don't sit around doing nothing all day, everyday. That would be boring. You have time to focus on things that you love. The people you love. And the activities that you love.

I started a podcast a few years ago. It was something I never would have had the bandwidth to do before minimalism. I wanted to help others along their journey towards minimalism. I get messages telling me how their lives have changed for the better because they released the clutter from their homes. With every episode, I think of it as spreading a softer, more gentle side of minimalism, one that isn't cold or extreme. Through my own journey, I have been able to create a ripple effect in the world, one household at a time.

Remember when I said that I felt like I was treading water all of the time? Minimalism felt like climbing into a boat after treading water for what seemed like forever. Imagine that for a second. The relief, the heaviness - lifted.

Minimalism helped me live a more intentional and slow life. I went from living in survival mode, under constant stress—to thriving.

I no longer have a full house, schedule and mind. I have a fulfilling life with less noise and distractions.

This life fills me up, that allows me to breathe, to enjoy, and to be energized… and it all started at home.

Perceptions
On Being Brave
Cheryl Magyar

I am a simplist. Not in the archaic meaning of "one who gathers medicinal herbs", though I am also an avid forager of wild healing plants. Yarrow, mugwort, plantain, nettle, chickweed, dandelion, cleavers, walnut leaf, shepherd's purse, willow bark, raspberry leaves and stems... They all hold an energetic space in the way we connect to the land and in how we choose to nurture ourselves. And that is where I becomes we. That magical series of moments where our lives became intertwined. Because without my husband and daughter, I would be a completely different person. Similar, though not quite the same me that is here today.

See, life is a journey. People say it all the time, yet part of me wonders if they truly honor this. If they deeply understand the importance of the series of nows that leads us to where we are in the present moment. It's a truly incredible and immensely powerful process, if you only stop to think about it. Along the way, we are met with happenings that can only bring about change. Sometimes, they are indeed life-changing. Preparing a week's worth of food over a woodstove when your home gets hit by lightning is one of them. Other times an event is merely a crossroads - a time to change direction and consciously choose to go another way: yours. When plans fail to go through, don't despair, something else is destined to come along, it always does. Which brings us to being brave in the face of an ever-changing life and climate.

Many people think that being brave is when you leave your place of birth, family, friends and familiar life, for one in a far off, unfamiliar place (say out in the plains of Hungary). It's brave when you sell your homestead and move to Scotland, with all you own on your back, including your four-year-old child whom you consciously birthed in the loving comfort of your own home.child whom you consciously birthed in the loving comfort of your own home. You are brave when you move to the edge of a village in northern Romania where the number of haystacks greatly outnumbers people. Where you see mountains, hills and forests in all directions, which sometimes makes it feel like you are living on the verge of the world. We are all these things and more, for which we have been called brave. Being brave is more than being courageous or daring, or perhaps just a little too adventurous. For when braveness is met with the heart, wonderful experiences can arise from the choices made in life.

To make a life story quick is no easy feat, let me be fearless here too. My origins start in a suburb of Chicago where I was born, though from a young age I loved to be outside: hiking, canoeing, swimming, camping, sitting by a campfire or in a tree with a good book. The bond to nature is strongest when formed at a young age, though it is never too late to start reconnecting to what should never be lost. My childhood dream was to move west, and so I did. Only to find love and get married in Las Vegas, trusting my intuition about the journey to come, now far east. It's been twenty remarkable years since.

Our simple life together began the moment we met. Ideas flowed back and forth, culminating into an eight-year move to the Hungarian countryside where we basked in quietude and gratitude. It was then and there, that living an intentional life, closer to nature than ever before, came into existence. We had snakes slither into our kitchen when the door was open, our pair of intrepid mangalica pigs came searching for us one day when we hadn't checked in on them. Three storks landed on the tile roof of our home just days before Csermely was born. Later, a gray heron stood a few feet from our front door, hours before we were meant to leave on the next passage of our lives. As if, to say goodbye, good luck, you were meant to take this flight.

During this homestead trial, we learned how to live with less than we'd ever had in our lives. Partly by circumstance, the rest by choice. We had a well for washing-up water and we rode bicycles a few kilometers away to fetch drinking water from an artesian well. We worked the soil, only until we learned about a no-dig approach to gardening. Through it all, we made mistakes in raising animals and in preserving food. Skills that we could have, should-have, gleaned from our ancestors were now found in books, as few were around to share their knowledge. The longer we walked barefoot, the deeper connection we felt to nature and the more we desired to live simply. Not only for the sake of others, even more so for the best interests of all life on Earth.

As life unfolded, we went from being consumers to creators. Initially, we embraced voluntary simplicity, then we became so-called eco-minimalists. But the latter wasn't our true calling. Measuring/weighing the amount of your belongings is fine if you are living out of a backpack, which we did for several years, though to live a marvelous life in tune with nature, one needs more. More space, more jars, more herbs, more tools than which one can carry. To homestead, one needs a garden and land to self-provide from, trees for food, furniture and shade, animals for deep nourishment and joy. At some point, the concept of minimalism fades away and leaves room for natural, simple living with just the right amount of overflowing fullness of everything. After all, there is no better place to look for abundance, than outside in nature.

Living an intentional life aligned with the seasons, means slowing down and embracing change. Sometimes it also means going against the flow of consumerism.

I don't believe we are brave because we dared to move lightly across countries and continents– migratory birds do it all the time. We feel ourselves to be brave for the simple truth that we dare to live our lives outside of the mainstream, not necessarily conform to societal expectations, yet always looking for alignment with nature, the Earth, the Universe. When you resist buying everything new, when you rewear an outfit, when you sew your own clothes, when you preserve your own pickles and jams, when you grow your own food, when you create your own job so you can work from home as you watch over your growing children, when you make your own herbal remedies to heal yourself, when you take care of what you watch and what you think, so that your energy is best aligned with that of the Earth, then you are brave too. The truth is, it takes work (and money) to live a simple, intentional life in a world that is over-complicated, over-computerized and overrun with being busy. Imagine if you took one small step, each and every day, to reduce and finally eliminate the overwhelm of modern life. Would you be less stressed? Would you be happier/healthier? Would you be a soothing island of calm amidst the burning chaos? One of the best parts about life is that you get to choose. You get to hand-pick your future. To do that takes intention. So be intent, be purposeful, be bold. As we have recently learned, "where intention goes, energy flows".

There's a little bit of braveness in all of us, oftentimes it is patiently waiting to be discovered.

Conscious Simplicity
An Invitation to Come Home to Myself
Krista O'Reilly-Davi-Digui

I'm not convinced life has to be quite as complicated as we make it. We don't control every circumstance, and life can be incredibly hard at times, but most of us still have at least some room to choose who we want to be and how we want to show up to life. We have freedom to play within the various limitations of our life. Partly as a values-based choice, in part by necessity, I opt for a slow, simple, and sustainable way of moving through the world; a lifestyle that helps me feel safe and at home in my body and my life.

Conscious simplicity allows me to live with purpose, health, and joy, reduce my environmental footprint, and contribute intentionally. It helps me sift through all the noise, the "shoulds" and shiny opportunities, to tell the truth about what I most want and need, and how I hope to use my small gifts to help build a kinder, safer world. It creates natural boundaries that help me walk out my values, honor my wiring, lean into my strengths, and reduce comparison, perfectionism, and fear.

But I don't think we should confuse simple with easy.

Simple is not synonymous with easy for many reasons. To begin with, life doesn't care what declarations we make; it will give us opportunities to stretch and grow. There is no magic "simple bubble" that protects us from all pain. Time and again we are invited to choose our path forward: we can run, numb, or distract ourselves or we can say yes to stretching and learning to be with discomfort. While simple living does not protect us from this reality, it does free up emotional, energetic, and financial resources to deal with life's challenges when they arise.

Next, I'm not pursuing easy because I'm clear that the life I want, and the kind of person I choose to be - whole, brave, rooted, and unshackled - requires conscious effort. Living in integrity, truth-telling, and showing up fully to life in every season means doing hard things on a daily basis. Rarely have I ever found living easy.

My 23-year-old son ended his life 21 months ago after a long, brave, and ferocious battle with severe depression and persistent suicidality. Every hour at first, then every day since he left this world, I've needed to "say yes to life" all over again. By this, I mean to all of life: to the joy and delight, and to the heart-wrenching sorrow, searing anguish, and impossible letting go. A practice of simplicity, including the habit of identifying "my enough" in every season, a belief in our interdependence and willingness to ask for and receive help, and permission to rest, has helped keep me anchored through the fiercest storm of my life.

Simple does not automatically mean easy and it also does not mean concession or settling as some people believe. It's weird to me that people think you're "playing small" if you have the talent or means to work as a doctor or engineer, for example, but choose a more values-aligned path, or if you opt for "enough" over bigger and better. Accolades, titles, financial wealth, and acquisition do not automatically confer happiness or meaning. Just because we can do something doesn't mean we should. Pushing back against the status quo to walk out our values requires inner strength and clear conviction.

A simple life comes in many shapes and sizes and will evolve with us across the seasons of our life. We have the privilege and responsibility to re-envision our lives as we go. It seems that being human would feel easier if we ever could "arrive" but as long as we have breath within us, we are called deeper not wider. Every season offers new lessons and gifts, but we have to work for them even if that simply means saying yes to living fully awake, present, and willing. Saying yes to receiving.

Having said this, choosing simple does make my life easier (not easy, but easier) than if I were constantly trying to measure up or keep up, or filling my life to overflowing without pausing to consider why. There is certainly more ease and calm in filtering and sifting, keeping my eyes on my own path, and handcrafting a brave life, one step and one breath at a time.

*　　*　　*　　*

Experiences of trauma and profound grief, chronic physical pain and struggles with my mental health, have helped me surrender to the temporal nature of this life. Nothing lasts forever. Spring always comes again. This moment is fleeting.

I aim to receive, arms and heart wide-open, the gift of each new day. The gift of the people who share life with me each day. I hold a clear and compelling vision for my life and take slow and steady action to bring my vision to fruition. This is less about an external destination (though certainly I have goals I'm working toward) and more about a daily reminder to BE who I want to be. Today. To stop deferring joy. To love myself exactly as I am at this moment. To pause and notice all the beauty tangled up in this messy and imperfect life of mine, right now, in the middle of the storm.

In this middle season of my life, conscious simplicity looks and feels like space to breathe, travel, and rest. Permission to grieve without rules or timelines, to create, play, savor, use my voice, and do work that lights me up with less attachment to outcome. It includes constantly stripping away past the point of comfort for my ego, leaning into my strengths, celebrating my hard work, and writing a new hopeful story for the next season of my life.

In this season, simple living also means plenty of nos. Letting go of performing or pleasing others at the expense of my well-being, shoring up leaky boundaries. It includes saying no to many wonderful opportunities to focus on my highest priorities including healing and connecting with my favorite people.

And it involves carefully protecting my precious freedom to tilt and flex when my family needs more of me or when I notice a need to attend more to my mind-body-spirit health.

Conscious simplicity has always worked best, for me, with self-imposed rules that reduce decision fatigue and wrestling. Some examples include a no-bullying policy (I only speak to myself with kindness), choosing a minimalist wardrobe, and monthly principal-only payments to shave 7 years off the life of my mortgage, even though there have been times that money would have come in handy. I don't have to argue with myself about these things; I make a decision once, and then walk it out daily. Simple. Not easy.

Similarly, the daily, weekly, and yearly rhythms I've set in motion in addition to my framework of seasonal living, allow for not only a simpler, but also a gentler and more compassionate way of being. There is room here for ebb and flow. Space for me to deepen self-awareness and become more fully myself. As much as possible, I work with instead of against my natural wiring, which includes introversion, high-sensitivity, and thriving with white space to putter, learn, and think. When I am filled up and whole, I am resourced to engage outwardly and pour out.

*   *   *   *

Slow and simple living means showing up present and mindful and not rushing through my days. Not even the painful ones. Listening inward and mining for the beauty and wisdom knit into every season. Life is not a race to the finish line nor an upward climb, but a messy gift to be unwrapped with great delight, or an invitation to grow downward, "towards the roots of one's being" as author, mythologist, and storyteller Michael Meade writes in Why the World Doesn't End: Tales of Renewal in Times of Loss. Simplicity cuts through all the noise, beckons and accompanies me as I do the brave and soul-stretching work of coming home to myself. "Slowing downwards creates opportunities to dwell more deeply in one's life, for the home we are looking for in this world is within us all along," Meade proposes.

Realizing that simple doesn't mean easy brings freedom. It means you're not doing it wrong if, try as you might, life keeps throwing you curve-balls. It means you can be proud of yourself for showing up imperfectly on purpose and taking small, consistent steps to build a life and world you want to live in. Perfection ought never be the goal. Easy is not the goal. Conforming to someone else's path or standard is clearly not the goal.

Living conscious and awake, risking saying yes to a gentle, mindful, messy life that feels like home, this is the goal, at least for me.

More

Ellie Roscher

My great-grandparents John and Helen were both from big families, their respective parents immigrated from Poland to St. Paul, Minnesota. My great-grandfather John ran his own printing business and Helen cleaned other people's houses. My grandpa Mark came home from half-day kindergarten at St. Albert's, where they spoke Polish, to an empty house. Sometimes he felt scared, and sat behind a big chair, waiting there until his big brother came home from school later in the afternoon. During The Depression, the two boys followed coal trucks through the bumpy streets, picking up the pieces that dropped off the bed to bring home.

Carol was the love of Mark's life, but she was not Catholic, so he married my grandma Peg instead. Peg's mom Delia, my great-grandma, was the oldest of nine girls and the first from her family to leave Ireland. She pulled my grandma out of secondary school and sent her to work in her dad's office to verify if he was having an affair. Peg was eighteen when her family moved from St. Paul to Chicago. She decided to stay back in St. Paul alone.

My mom Margaret was the fourth of six kids. In kindergarten, she got dressed, fixed herself breakfast and left for school on her own. My grandpa was already at his first of two jobs and my grandma was still in bed. By age twelve, my mom babysat every Friday and Saturday night for $0.50 an hour. She bought her own shampoo and clothes. In the summer, she watched four kids from 6:30am-4:30pm. Over time she took on jobs at a bakery, then pharmacy, then hospital, paying her way through private high school and college.

My first job was babysitting as well and soon after, at age fourteen, I started coaching pre-school gymnastics. Like my mom, I liked putting the money I earned straight into the bank. Unlike my mom, I didn't need it to get by.

I am the second of five kids, and we never worried about money. My dad decided to be a dentist, in part because my parents wanted to provide more for their family than their parents did. More for them meant more financial stability. I grew up with a bigger financial safety net than my ancestors or parents. I was afforded a childhood of stability and ease, and I am grateful. As I grew, the safety net created space to wonder, "What does more mean for me and my children?"

Curating a life of simplicity started from a place of privilege. I was acutely aware that I was born into a family with more financial stability than others. I experimented with what I wanted versus what I needed. In defining enough as just the right amount, I used joy, ease, and a sense of lightness as a barometer. Objects have a weight, as do our relationships to them. After college, I joined intentional communities that valued simplicity. I moved abroad to immerse myself in cultures that defined "enough" differently. Because I always had enough money, I could see that after a certain point, more stuff did not equate to more happiness. I could see that by watching my parents.

When I was twelve, my parents bought a plot of land and built a large house. My mom admits now that was a mistake for her personality. She saw the house as an external mark of her work. It was her job to keep it from depreciating. When the house starts brand new and is filled with five small children, perfection was an impossible standard. Every scratch happened on her watch. She cleaned the house daily. There were two rooms we couldn't go in. As a child, there were times I wondered if she loved the house more than me.

As an adult, I signed lease after lease, scared to own my own house. I defined home as my body, as the world my spouse and I created between us. Eventually my friend from one of my intentional communities reminded me, "You own the house. Just don't let the house own you." After fifteen different rentals, while pregnant with my first child, we bought an old house, with layers of paint and dirt that didn't accumulate on my watch. I worked up the courage to grow roots there woven with memories and love.

*   *   *   *

In my early thirties I had two miscarriages in the same year. I wanted to be a mom so badly that the desire for what I didn't have consumed me. I walked through my days in a cloud of not-enough-ness. The losses wrecked me and reminded me of what I already knew: we can spend our entire lives striving and wanting. We can perpetually fling ourselves into the past and the future, opting out of the present. We can pine for a different life, a life we thought would be ours. Or we can sit in our vulnerability and mortality, in the broken messy beauty of the world and intentionally choose to fall in love with the life that is right in front of us. When we let the desire for more drop away, what is left is simply what is, in all its mundane and mediocre, spectacular and glorious beauty.

One child grew inside me, entering the world with the most luminous face I had ever seen. Then another child came, luscious and beaming. They took my breath away. I longed for them even as they rolled around in front of me. With the arrival of children comes the incessant invitation for more gear, more toys, and more calendar invites. There is a constant pressure to provide the very best for your children, to give them more than you had. Instead of more, I doubled down on enough. They taught me in their effortless presence that home is my body and my family, yes. And home is also the present moment. This breath. Home is where all your attempts to escape cease.

I practice intentionality and simplicity because I want to live this life well. I don't want to miss it. I don't want to accept the endless invitations to exist in the past or the future, or to busy myself with managing my relationship to stuff. As loving my children, my spouse, my found family and increasingly myself, takes up more and more space in my life, the other stuff falls away. My work is to hold onto objects and calendar invites lightly, without clinging. It is to dwell in just the right amountness so that I exude a sense of lightness and ease in my days. My work is to remember I am not more by doing more or having more. I can honor the noble striving of my ancestors and parents to provide more money by living in the joy that now, for me more money is not, in fact, the goal. Less stuff expands my capacity to listen deeply, to love fiercely, and to opt into the moment right in front of me.

Ultimately, I practice intentionality and simplicity because I want to die well. When I am brave enough to claim sparseness in my calendar, closet, garage, and to-do list, the buzz quiets. In the silence, I remember I am mortal, which in turn reminds me to live. Dying well is tied to living well, to actively being astonished with the life that is right in front of me. To paying attention to life as it is being lived. My more has become more love. My more is defining home as the present moment. In releasing my grip on the striving to do more and have more. It is cultivating a life I do not want to escape, where my sense of enough is contributing to the possibility of communal peace where everyone belongs and everyone has enough.

Seeking contentment in this breath, I find the bliss of eternal contentment. Contentment is the inheritance I hope to embody and pass on as my more.

Living Slower
to Heal from Trauma
Emma Scheib

For as long as I can remember, being busy has served a soothing and protective role in my life. Busyness was the socially acceptable drug that I used to band-aid the wounds I'd acquired from significant, chronic, developmental and childhood trauma. When I was busy seeking approval, gaining perfect grades, and chasing the next bright, shiny thing, I couldn't hear the screaming inside my head. But busyness only muffled the screaming and the effects of the trauma emerged as other things like anxiety, alcohol dependence and an eating disorder.

At the height of my busyness addiction I was numbing the incessant screaming with a masters degree, full time work, and training for a half ironman race. When things got too quiet I would add another layer. Volunteer for something, bake cookies for the masses. Anything to ensure I didn't have to face the growing evidence that there was something that I desperately needed to face.

Without going into too much detail (to protect the privacy of my family), there are two main traumas that I've lived through. The first was being adopted at 10 days old. Without undermining the good intentions of both my birth mother, who felt she couldn't give me the life I deserved, and my adopted parents, who couldn't conceive, the fact remains - I suffered a significant, deep attachment wound.

*   *   *   *

The second trauma was the ongoing chaos that ensued from my adopted brother and I dealing with these attachment wounds. Unfortunately for my brother and our family this meant him being diagnosed with a variety of disorders including conduct disorder and attention deficit disorder.

His trauma had him act out, often very aggressively, until he was finally removed from our home by social welfare services at age thirteen.

Trauma, upon trauma. A thick web of events and emotional consequences that no one in the 1980's knew what to do with.

However my body and brain knew what to do. To use Bessel Van der Kolk's term, my 'body kept the score' with a seemingly constant array of physical illnesses, and my brain kept me busy so I could avoid any more emotional pain.

And it all worked well. Until it didn't.

When I began reading about trauma a few years ago, I was surprised to learn of both the nuances and the prevalence of it.

Trauma was a far more common and complex human experience than I had ever been led to believe. It permeated most of the cracks in society. I went from thinking it was usually the result of a one off event, like being in a car crash, to realizing it was almost everywhere.

The lifetime prevalence of receiving a diagnosis of PTSD after a traumatic event is estimated at between 6 and 9 percent in the general population. For complex PTSD, which occurs after exposure to long lasting and repeated trauma over months or years, the prevalence is around 4 percent.

Trauma is generally regarded as a subjective and individually defined event. And additionally, research has highlighted the effects of numerous types of insidious, or hidden trauma, like microaggressions from racism, to the list of examples of types of trauma one can experience.

Experiencing trauma, in some form, to some extent, is a common human experience.

I often quote my 'official' start on the slow and simple journey as a moment in bed, pregnant with my second child, googling 'how to slow down'. I was exhausted and unsure I could continue at the pace I was living.

For some reason the memory of that moment is burned deep in my psyche. I don't remember any specifics about the day, just the undeniable knowing that I needed to stop.

This journey had begun before that moment though, and as most journeys do, it was made up of moments across my entire lifespan. Moments where my intuition told me something wasn't right. I had felt a sort of cognitive dissonance for a long time, without being able to pinpoint exactly what it was about.

The bed moment was a moment of clarity. I was broken by my busyness and if I wanted to salvage and piece together the remaining bits of myself I needed to slow down. Way down.

This was my signpost, my fork in the road, and one of my dark nights of the soul (I am a great believer that we are blessed with more than one of these).

*   *   *   *

After long-term complex trauma there were lots of bits and pieces of myself that needed picking up and tending to. This takes time. And to really heal, it takes a purposeful slowing down of what time I have.

Active noticing has become one of the most important tools for my slower pace of life. In relation to my trauma, the end goal is that I am able to notice my feelings, without numbing them. Observe them, without wanting to rush to their aid all the time.

And it starts with adding small moments of active noticing into my everyday life. What does my coffee really taste like? What does the air outside smell of? What is my back ache telling me?

Small but powerful steps to a more awake, aware and intentional life. And eventually, a life that is less negatively affected by my history of trauma.

In a more practical sense, I go slower by saying no more often. No to anything that takes my time away from the most important things. My healing journey and my family.

So no, I won't go to that party that will leave me socially exhausted and wanting to hide in the closet for days. No to back-to-back appointments and meetings and catch-ups. No to a perfect house and four different kinds of vegetables every night. No to keeping up with the Joneses, and no (as much as I can muster) to tending to my wounds using alcohol, exercise or excessive social media consumption.

And then a courageous resounding yes to making space for picking myself up off the floor, and cobbling the bits back together.

This means attending regular therapy sessions, and working outside of these sessions to educate myself and put into practice what I'm learning.

It also means building practices that will create new ways of supporting my nervous system when life inevitably tempts me with busyness again, or when I can't avoid a busier period. For me this is yoga, walking meditation, mindfulness exercises, and rest. And lots of time in nature. Being outside, immersed in the natural world is, in my humble opinion, one of the best ways to calibrate a nervous system that has been through trauma.

*   *   *   *

I won't be put back together in the same way as before. This is what trauma does. It alters things for good. Forever, and for good. My trauma is a part of me and it's shaping me into something new and good.

My journey to a slower pace of life has given me the opportunity to do deep self exploration that I wouldn't have done if I didn't slow down. It's offered me an opportunity to heal and grow into the human I am meant to be.

And through it all I hope to pave a way for my own daughters to see and appreciate a life that's not focused on work, and busyness. I hope to inspire them to do whatever it takes to grow into the kind of humans that they are meant to be.

Reverence and Responsibility
Living a Simple, Sustainable Life
Gail Straub

> For the moment all you have to know is that two funda-
> mentally different stories have been enacted here during
> the lifetime of [humans]. One began to be enacted here
> some two or three million years ago by the people we've
> agreed to call Leavers and is still being enacted by them
> today, as successfully as ever. The other began to be enacted
> here some ten or twelve thousand years ago by the people
> we've agreed to call Takers and is apparently about to end
> in catastrophe.
>
> —ISHMAEL, BY DANIEL QUINN

In his visionary novel Ishmael, Daniel Quinn demonstrates
that our cultural story, our shared set of cultural assumptions,
operates on the premise that evolution ended with the appearance of humans. Rather than acknowledging that we are
just the latest chapter in a mysterious ongoing saga, we humans think and act as if the story has ended with us—as if
we are somehow above or outside the evolutionary tale. And

in operating as if evolution doesn't exist for us we are, sadly, taking actions that could actually make this true. Because of our consumption patterns, humans have been responsible for the extinction of one million species. Meanwhile it has taken the earth 4.5 billion years to create its intricate web of life with myriad species. And in particular, despite being a small 5 percent of the world's human population, Americans consume one third of the planet's resources. While U.S. citizens use up to three times more than our fair share, at least a billion people in the rest of the world aren't getting enough food to survive.

My husband David and I have led a simple sustainable lifestyle during our forty years together because we aspire to be "Leavers" not "Takers." And as a leader in the climate-change sector David empowers both individuals and cities to be Leavers. For my part, after all these years I have concluded that I am living intentionally when action and contemplation are in partnership, when responsibility and reverence are held in equal regard. I experience the fullest meaning as well as the fullest impact of simple living when my sustainable acts are imbued with spiritual practice. Each of my earth-friendly behaviors—reusing, recycling, repairing, eco-wise shopping, composting, conserving water and energy—is also an act of mindfulness. My spiritual practice motivates pragmatic responsibility, and responsible action invigorates my reverence for the sacredness of life. Over the years, having a stewardship ethic has helped me simplify my life, and allowed for prioritizing (and reprioritizing) the things that really matter to me—including creativity, community, service, time spent in nature, and space for long-forgotten dreams. As an antidote to the addictions of both distraction and consumerism, simple living heals the spiritual emptiness at the core of so many lives.

For many of us the most profound motivation for living intentionally comes from the earth itself. When we spend time in the natural world—reclaiming intimacy with rivers, mountains, stones, forest, desert, ocean, and creatures—we reconnect with the miraculous web of life that sustains us. In engaging with nature, we are uplifted by the great community of which we are but one member.

"Today we participate almost exclusively with other humans and with our own human-made technologies," says David Abram in his luminous book The Spell of the Sensuous. And he warns, "It is a precarious situation, given our age-old reciprocity with the many-voiced landscape. We still need that which is other than ourselves and our own creations. We are human only in contact, and conviviality, with that which is not human." This kinship with the earth that Abram advocates is intrinsically connected with our capacity to heal and to hope. And healing and hopefulness lead organically to responsibility.

Responsibility comes fully alive with the degree of mindfulness that I bring to my most ordinary daily acts of intentional living that determine the sacredness of life. Indeed, it is mindfulness that transforms the mundane into the sacred. Daily life offers opportunities to invoke the four elements—earth, air, water, and fire—starting with earth: When I recycle, reuse, repair, or compost, I offer each of these actions as prayers of gratitude for Gaia's stupendous generosity. Every time I purchase a green product, each time I share, loan, or swap instead of buying, I am imparting reverence to the earth. I am saying to the generations who follow me, I care about you, and I want you to have the resources that ensure life.

Turning to the element of air: with each action I make, large and small, to avoid fossil fuels—when I invest in a Tesla, cluster my errands and drive less, take public transportation, or choose to walk or ride a bike—I make an offering to clean, fresh air. I am saying to those I love, I want you to breathe free and easy.

Invoking the element of water: When I conserve water by taking a shorter shower, fixing a leak, or practicing xeriscaping, each of these ordinary actions connects me with those millions of people who don't have enough water. Each of these savings is offered to those who are dying or suffering from drought or polluted water.

And finally, the element of fire: My solar-powered house embodies my gratitude to the great fireball that sustains all existence. When I lower the heat, raise the temperature for the air-conditioning, or get an energy audit, each of these routine practices transforms the mundane into the sacred. Earth, air, water, and fire: without them there is no life.

Intentional living needs both the in-breath of mindfulness as well as the out-breath of pragmatic actions that create a sustainable lifestyle. Reverence is embodied as we take the humble, mindful steps to live more lightly on our planet. And over time ordinary acts of stewardship become sacred offerings to the living earth. The poet Basho encouraged us with these words: "Make the universe your companion, always bearing in mind the true nature of all creation—mountains and rivers, trees and grasses, and humankind."

To live intentionally, then, is to make the universe your companion.

Afterword
Why to Walk Slowly
Heidi Barr

Do you ever find yourself walking slowly, meandering, saun-
tering with no lofty goal? There are so many reasons a person
might take to the forest or prairie, or perhaps the beach or
desert. Even a suburban park or urban alleyway will do. When
we downshift from frantic running around (in all its modern
forms) to a slow walk, and really take the time to notice what's
going on, things come to light that wouldn't otherwise. I am
more apt to remember how it feels to move at a pace that feels
right and good, and do it more often. I am less likely to get
caught up in the trap of being productive at all costs. I am
able to take full breaths, and fill my lungs as they're meant to
be filled, instead of making them subsist on shallow gasps.
There are a lot of reasons to walk slowly, to pay attention to the
details, to emulate a snail's pace. Consider what good things
moving slow can bring about in life.

For me, that slow walk often takes place in the woods.

When I walk slowly, I see the tiny orange mushrooms that have taken up residence on the tops of three fallen oaks, enormous trees that crashed to earth years ago, that are now, in death covered with soft moss, green lichen, tiny orange mushrooms that look like they are just waiting for fairies to arrive for a festival of aliveness and wonder.

When I walk slowly, I can taste wild blackberries, the ones whose brambles tower high overhead and hang heavy with fruit in the late summer. Fingers stained purple, there are more berries here than any one creature needs, enough to eat a handful and pocket another for later. They taste like sunlight and wild nectar and joy in tiny purple offerings.

When I walk slowly, I can hear a breeze, one that's been dormant the last few stagnant days, rustling leaves on the mighty Maples of the forest, and it's like listening to a great chorus of gentle giants celebrating what life is like in the canopy.

When I walk slowly, I can feel the many feet of a tiny caterpillar, one that decides to crawl up my arm as I sit on an old stump by the lake, a tiny tickle on skin as the fuzzy black, yellow, and white being makes its own path on this new territory. Exploration completed after a few minutes, he steps off. I watch him make his way down the side of the stump and into the tall grass that leads him toward whatever comes next when you are a caterpillar in a woodland.

When I walk slowly, I smell the earthy loam underfoot, the musty aroma of the lake, the sharp scent of hot pine needles, the deep richness that is last year's leaves mixed with the moisture the forest floor produces in abundance, a hint of rain in the atmosphere, the way quickly running water of a tiny creek carries with it coolness that reminds me how refreshment can sneak up on a person via any of the senses, the salt in my own tears that seem to well up from somewhere unknown. After enough time has passed, the scent of wildness and humanness merges, remembrance falling together that all beings are part of the same body.

Ross Gay says, "Is sorrow the true wild?

And if it is—and if we join them—your wild to mine—what's that?

For joining, too, is a kind of annihilation.

What if we joined our sorrows, I'm saying.

I'm saying: What if that is joy?"

I walk slowly in the woods to remember to be alive with my whole self, to join those thickets of dense seemingly inaccessible wilds that live in each of us as sorrow, with something deeper than what I can access on my own. I walk slowly to claim the pace that serves my life best, one that allows a simple existence, one that is attuned to the joys and sorrows of an earthly life. I walk slowly to ensure my quest for a good life is met by enough joy to keep me going for another day.

There are a lot of reasons to walk slowly, be it through a forest or through life itself. May your reasons join with mine, those of all these other writers, and all the sorrows of the world as we continue the search for simple.

Contributors

Heidi Barr is a writer and wellness coach whose work is founded on a commitment to cultivating ways of being that are life-giving and sustainable for people, communities, and the planet. She is the author of three works of creative nonfiction: *Collisions of Earth and Sky*, *Woodland Manitou*, and *What Comes Next*; two poetry collections: *Slouching Toward Radiance* and *Cold Spring Hallelujah*; and one cookbook: *Prairie Grown: Stories and Recipes from a South Dakota Hillside*. She is also the coauthor of *12 Tiny Things* and editor of "The Mindful Kitchen," a wellness column in *The Wayfarer Magazine*. She lives with her family in rural Minnesota, where they tend a large vegetable garden, explore nature, and do their best to live simply. Learn more at heidibarr.com.

Gail Collins-Ranadive, MA, MFA, MDiv, is a nature-based author and climate activist. Her books include *Finding the Voice Inside, Writing as a Spiritual Quest for Women*; *Light Year*; *Chewing Sand: An Eco-Spiritual Taste of the Mojave Desert*; *Nature's Calling: The Grace of Place*; *A Fistful of Stars: Communing with the Cosmos*; and *Dinosaur Dreaming: Our Climate Moment*, along with two books for children. She sponsors The Prism Prize for Climate Literature and writes the environmental column for *The Wayfarer*, both part of Homebound Publications. Mother of two and grandmother of five, Gail spends summers at her partner's home in Denver, winters at her home in Las Vegas.

Stephen Drew lives in a bucolic lakeside community in north-western Connecticut. In addition to *Around the Forever Bend,* he also authored the memoir *Into the Thin: A Pilgrimage Walk Across Northern Spain* which was his first published work. Stephen practices a minimalist lifestyle which includes daily walking, mostly on the roads and paths near his home. Hiking there and elsewhere serves as a centerpiece of contemplative living and an ongoing connection to Source. He currently resides in Morris, Connecticut. Visit him at authorstephendrew.com.

Allison Sue Elliott is a personal growth enthusiast, journal lover, and intentional living devotee. She lives in Maryland with her husband, farm animals, and book collection. As the founder of *Compass My Life,* Allison Sue spends her work time helping others discover what intentional living means for them and how to navigate towards a life they feel good about.

Juliana Aragón Fatula is a poet, has been a writer in residence for Colorado Humanities' Writers in the Schools Program, and is a member of the Sandra Cisneros' Macondo Foundation: creative writers whose work is socially engaged and who view their writing as way of changing lives by fostering literacy. In 2022 she was inducted into the Return of the Corn Mothers Project, women who pull from the past all that is sacred and holy to create a future filled with promise. She is the author of *Crazy Chicana in Catholic City* and *Red Canyons Falling on Churches.* She lives in Cañon City, Colorado.

Angie Kikstra is the founder of Cozy Minimalism and host of the Cozy Minimalism podcast. She believes that creating a home that allows you to rest, relax and unwind is necessary in to-day's world. She emphasizes that minimalism doesn't have to feel cold, and cozy doesn't have to feel cluttered. Learn more about how to remove clutter in layers and create your haven at home by visiting cozyminimal.com

Joseph Little is an English professor at Niagara University in Lewiston, New York. His most recent creative work is *Letters from the Other Side of Silence*, published by Homebound Publications in 2017.

Cheryl Magyar is a freelance writer, sustainable lifestyle designer, no-dig organic gardener, forager, horticulturist and simplist. From her chosen "home"stead in northern Romania, along with her husband and homeschooled daughter, she inspires individuals, families and small businesses to return to simpler ways of life - in accordance with the cycles of nature. She me-anders barefoot on the land, takes cold baths in the creek and walks gently through the forest, dreaming of rewilding large swaths of it one day, soon. From reintroducing beavers and European bison, to planting thousands of native trees, the vi-sion is clear. Follow the journey at ForestCreekMeadows.com.

Gunilla Norris has been a psychotherapist in private practice for more than thirty years and has felt privileged to accompany many people on their journeys to growth and healing. Her special love has been teaching meditation and leading con-templative workshops of many kinds. As a writer Gunilla has published eleven children's books, one book of poetry and six books on spirituality including: *Being Home, Becoming Bread, Inviting Silence, A Mystic Garden, Simple Ways* and *Sheltered in the Heart,*

Krista O'Reilly Davi-Digui (she/her) works as a writer, Holistic Embodiment Coach + Joyful Living Educator. She helps her clients and community members learn to feel safe, at home + joyful in their body and their life in every season. Even the hardest of them. She lives near the Rocky Mountains in Canada. Connect with her at alifeinprogress.ca, at facebook.com/alifeinprogressca, and on Instagram @a_life_in_progress.

Ellie Roscher is the author of *The Embodied Path, Play Like a Girl,* and *How Coffee Saved My Life* as well as coauthor of *12 Tiny Things.* She hosts the Unlikely Conversations podcast and teaches writing and yoga at The Loft Literary Center, the Minnesota Writing Project, and Up Yoga. She has an MFA in Creative Nonfiction Writing from Sarah Lawrence College as well as an MA in Theology from Luther Seminary. She lives in Minneapolis with her spouse and sons. Visit her at ellieroscher.com.

Emma Scheib is a mom and writer. Her blog, Simple Slow & Lovely, helps people live a slower, simpler, and intentional life, based on their values. She is a highly sensitive introvert who loves helping others like her find strength and joy through boundaries and self exploration. As a self prescribed multipotiante her interests range from the macabre like taxidermy and true crime, to how trees talk to each other. Based in New Zealand, she is determined to change the world one sentence at a time. Learn more at simpleslowlovely.com.

Gail Straub is the author of six books including the best-selling *Empowerment* translated into over fourteen languages, the critically acclaimed *The Rhythm of Compassion* and the award-winning *The Ashokan Way: Landscape's Path into Consciousness*. An activist and pioneer in the field of empowerment, she co-directs the Empowerment Institute where for over three decades she has offered her work to tens of thousands of people worldwide. She co-founded IMAGINE: A Global Initiative for the Empowerment of Women currently in Africa, Afghanistan, India, and the Middle East. Gail Straub lives in the Hudson River Valley in New York. Visit her at .empowermentinstitute.net

HOMEBOUND
PUBLICATIONS

Since 2011 We are an award-winning independent publisher striving to ensure that the mainstream is not the only stream. More than a company, we are a community of writers and readers exploring the larger questions we face as a global village. It is our intention to preserve contemplative storytelling. We publish full-length introspective works of creative non-fiction, literary fiction, and poetry.

Look for Our Imprints Little Bound Books, Owl House Books, *The Wayfarer Magazine,* Wayfarer Books & Navigator Graphics

WWW.HOMEBOUNDPUBLICATIONS.COM

WAYFARER

BASED IN THE BERKSHIRE MOUNTAINS, MASS.

The Wayfarer Magazine. Since 2012, *The Wayfarer* has been offering literature, interviews, and art with the intention to inspires our readers, enrich their lives, and highlight the power for agency and change-making that each individual holds. By our definition, a wayfarer is one whose inner-compass is ever-oriented to truth, wisdom, healing, and beauty in their own wandering. *The Wayfarer's* mission as a publication is to foster a community of contemplative voices and provide readers with resources and perspectives that support them in their own journey.

Wayfarer Books is our newest imprint! After nearly 10 years in print, *The Wayfarer Magazine* is branching out from our magazine to become a full-fledged publishing house offering full-length works of eco-literature!

Wayfarer Farm & Retreat is our latest endeavor, springing up the Berkshire Mountains of Massachusetts. Set to open to the public in 2025, the 15-acre retreat will offer workshops, farm-to-table dinners, off-grid retreat cabins, and artist residencies.

CPSIA information can be obtained
at www.ICGtesting.com
Printed in the USA
LVHW031057240223
740091LV00001B/67